Special Occasion Memories

A Written Legacy

For a dear friend — I hope you have many wonderful special occasions in your life.

Kim E. Kimmy

Conceived and created by

KIM E. KIMMY

Illustrated by Hannah June

Published by EDK Books and
Distributed by EDK Distribution, LLC
edkbookdistribution.com
edkbooksanddistribution@gmail.com
(206) 227-8179

Special Occasion Memories
Copyright © 2020 by Kim E. Kimmy

10 9 8 7 6 5 4 3 2 1

Printed in the United States of America

ISBN: 978-1-7339618-5-1

Editor: Barbara Kindness
Illustrator: Hannah June
Production: Melissa Vail Coffman

This book belongs to:

We all have special occasions to acknowledge throughout our lifetime. Though many are memorable because they are joyous, moments of achievement or noteworthy accomplishment, some may be remembrances of a special person at a memorial celebration, or public ceremony.

This book is to be a special keepsake because it will highlight the individual author's most heartfelt moments: birthdays, weddings, christenings, bar/bat mitzvahs, graduations, Independence Day, citizenship ceremony, Hanukkah, —whatever event that is meaningful to you or your loved ones. Included is space for photos, invitations, ticket stubs, and any mementos, too.

Enjoy this special book to remind yourself and loved ones now and in the future of special occasions and your way of celebrating them.

And, when you write something in your own handwriting, that too leaves a legacy for all to see.

Kim

— Some Special Occasion Ideas —

Anniversary

Athletic Achievement

Award

Baptism

Bar/Bat Mitzvah

Birth

Birthday

Change of Command Ceremony

Christening

Christmas

Cinco di Mayo

Citizenship

Commissioning Ceremony

Competition

Easter

Engagement

Confirmation

Father's Day

First Day of School

First Haircut

Halloween

Hanukkah

Housewarming

Independence Day

Initiation

Memorial Day

Mother's Day

First Communion

New Car

New Year Celebrations

Parades

Passover

Graduation

Homecoming

Prom

Performance

Recital

Reunion

Shower

Sporting Event

Kwanzaa

Thanksgiving

Tooth Fairy Visit

Vacation

Valentine's Day

Wedding

— Contents —

Occasion #1:

Day, Date & Time: Weather:

Location:

Who Was Present:

Activities:

There are exactly as many special occasions in life as we choose to celebrate.

—Robert Breault

 *Photos*

Enter the occasion, date, who is in the photo, and the photographer.

Decorations

Special or surprising thing(s) that happened
Toast, prayer, funny mishap...

Photos & Mementos

Tickets, certificates, ribbons...

Attire

 Photos

Notable Gifts/Presentations

Toast given by, prayer given by...

Memorable comments heard—and overheard

Food & Drink

Photos

─ *Best Memory from This Event* ─

Occasion #2

Day, Date & Time:

Weather:

Location:

Who Was Present:

Activities:

We must find time to stop and thank the people who make a difference in our lives.

—John F. Kennedy

 *Photos*

Enter the occasion, date, who is in the photo, and the photographer.

Decorations

Special or surprising thing(s) that happened
Toast, prayer, funny mishap...

Photos & Mementos

Tickets, certificates, ribbons...

Attire

 *Photos*

Notable Gifts/Presentations
Toast given by, prayer given by...

Memorable comments heard—and overheard

Food & Drink

Photos

— Best Memory from This Event —

Occasion #3

Day, Date & Time: Weather:

Location:

Who Was Present:

Activities:

A good life is a collection of happy moments.

—Dennis Waitley

 *Photos*

Enter the occasion, date, who is in the photo, and the photographer.

Decorations

Special or surprising thing(s) that happened

Toast, prayer, funny mishap...

Photos & Mementos

Tickets, certificates, ribbons...

Attire

 *Photos*

Notable Gifts/Presentations
Toast given by, prayer given by...

Memorable comments heard—and overheard

Food & Drink

Photos

— Best Memory from This Event —

Occasion #4

Day, Date & Time: Weather:

Location:

Who Was Present:

Activities:

The more you praise and celebrate your life, the more there is in life to celebrate.

—Oprah Winfrey

 *Photos*

Enter the occasion, date, who is in the photo, and the photographer.

Decorations

Special or surprising thing(s) that happened

Toast, prayer, funny mishap...

Photos & Mementos

Tickets, certificates, ribbons...

Attire

 **Photos**

Notable Gifts/Presentations

Toast given by, prayer given by...

Memorable comments heard—and overheard

Food & Drink

Photos

— Best Memory from This Event —

Occasion #5

Day, Date & Time:

Weather:

Location:

Who Was Present:

Activities:

I come from a family where gravy is considered a beverage.

—Erma Bombeck

 *Photos*

Enter the occasion, date, who is in the photo, and the photographer.

Decorations

Special or surprising thing(s) that happened
Toast, prayer, funny mishap...

Photos & Mementos

Tickets, certificates, ribbons...

Attire

 *Photos*

Notable Gifts/Presentations

Toast given by, prayer given by...

Memorable comments heard—and overheard

Food & Drink

Photos

— Best Memory from This Event —

Occasion #6

Day, Date & Time: Weather:

Location:

Who Was Present:

Activities:

Celebrate the happiness that friends are always giving.

—Amanda Bradley

 *Photos*

Enter the occasion, date, who is in the photo, and the photographer.

Decorations

Special or surprising thing(s) that happened
Toast, prayer, funny mishap...

Photos & Mementos

Tickets, certificates, ribbons...

Attire

 *Photos*

Notable Gifts/Presentations

Toast given by, prayer given by...

Memorable comments heard—and overheard

Food & Drink

Photos

— Best Memory from This Event —

Occasion #7

Day, Date & Time: Weather:

Location:

Who Was Present:

Activities:

Start living now. Stop saving the good china for that special occasion.

—Mary Ann Morrissey

 *Photos*

Enter the occasion, date, who is in the photo, and the photographer.

Decorations

Special or surprising thing(s) that happened

Toast, prayer, funny mishap...

Photos & Mementos

Tickets, certificates, ribbons...

Attire

 *Photos*

Notable Gifts/Presentations

Toast given by, prayer given by...

Memorable comments heard—and overheard

Food & Drink

Photos

— Best Memory from This Event —

Occasion #8

Day, Date & Time: Weather:

Location:

Who Was Present:

Activities:

Being alive is the special occasion.

—Mary Engelbreit

 *Photos*

Enter the occasion, date, who is in the photo, and the photographer.

Decorations

 ## Special or surprising thing(s) that happened
Toast, prayer, funny mishap...

Photos & Mementos

Tickets, certificates, ribbons...

Attire

 *Photos*

Notable Gifts/Presentations
Toast given by, prayer given by...

Memorable comments heard—and overheard

Food & Drink

Photos

— Best Memory from This Event —

Occasion #9

Day, Date & Time: Weather:

Location:

Who Was Present:

Activities:

Easter egg hunts prove your kids can find things when they really want to.

—Anonymous

 *Photos*

Enter the occasion, date, who is in the photo, and the photographer.

Decorations

 # Special or surprising thing(s) that happened

Toast, prayer, funny mishap…

Photos & Mementos

Tickets, certificates, ribbons...

Attire

*Photos*

Notable Gifts/Presentations

Toast given by, prayer given by...

Memorable comments heard—and overheard

Food & Drink

Photos

— Best Memory from This Event —

Occasion #10

Day, Date & Time: Weather:

Location:

Who Was Present:

Activities:

Cinderella never asked for a prince. She asked for a night off and a dress.

—Kiera Cass

 *Photos*

Enter the occasion, date, who is in the photo, and the photographer.

Decorations

Special or surprising thing(s) that happened
Toast, prayer, funny mishap...

Photos & Mementos

Tickets, certificates, ribbons...

Attire

 *Photos*

Notable Gifts/Presentations
Toast given by, prayer given by...

Memorable comments heard—and overheard

Food & Drink

Photos

— Best Memory from This Event —

Special Recipes
... and how they were acquired

More Recipes

More Recipes

More Happy Memories

Keepsakes, mementos, photos...

More Happy Memories

Keepsakes, mementos, photos...

More Happy Memories

Keepsakes, mementos, photos...

More Happy Memories

Keepsakes, mementos, photos...

Ideas for Future Events

Wish I'd known then what I know now!

-
-
-
-
-
-
-
-
-
-
-
-
-
-
-
-